D1412597

Meet Oscar
the pumping unit with a big smile.

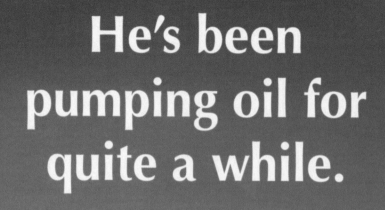

Oil makes gas.

Oil makes balloons.

There even is oil in your mom's shampoo!

as he put his hard hat on his head.

"You see, without pumpers like you and Bob, there would be nothing to fix and and I wouldn't have a job.

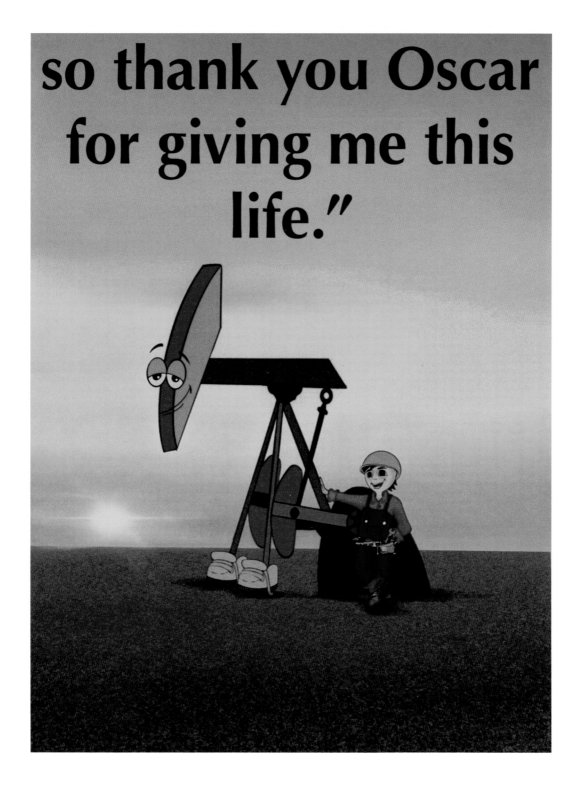

Made in the USA
Coppell, TX
24 March 2021

52282519R00017